Tracy Beaker Gets Real

A musical

Book and lyrics by Mary Morris
Music and additional lyrics by Grant Olding
Based on the novel *The Story of Tracy Beaker*
by Jacqueline Wilson

Samuel French — London
www.samuelfrench-london.co.uk

FOR AMATEUR PRODUCTION ENQUIRIES

UNITED KINGDOM AND WORLD EXCLUDING NORTH AMERICA
plays@samuelfrench.co.uk
020 7255 4302/01

Each title is subject to availability from Samuel French,
depending upon country of performance.

TRACY BEAKER GETS REAL

First performed by Nottingham Playhouse Theatre
Company at Nottingham Playhouse on 25th August
2006 prior to a tour with the following cast and
creative team:

Tracy Beaker	Sarah Churm
Mum/Louise	Jessica Martin
Cam	Alice Redmond
Justine Littlewood	Suzie McGrath
Peter	Andy Steed
Elaine the Pain	Gemma Page
Justine's Dad	Kirris Riviere

Musicians:	
Musical director and keyboards	Dean Austin
Guitars	Phil James
Keyboards	Toby Higgins

Directed by David Newman
Designed by Paul Wills
Lighting design by Guy Hoare
Composed and orchestrated by Grant Olding
Sound design by Adam McReady

CHARACTERS

Throughout the play the characters go back and forward in time to show the events in their past. If a large young cast is wanted the director may choose to cast a young Tracy and an older Tracy. Ditto the other young characters. Extra non-speaking "kids" can be cast if desired.

Tracy Beaker, 15 in the scenes set in the present. 10 - 11 in the early past scenes and 14-15 in the recent past scenes (from Act II, Scene 8). Exhausting, rude, cheeky, angry and beguiling.

Justine Littlewood, same ages as Tracy. Haughty, smart, and nearly as evil as Tracy.

Peter, a year younger than Tracy. Quiet, easily shoved around, but he will follow his star — when he finds out where it is.

Louise, same age as Tracy. A pretty girl who wants everyone to be happy and get along. (Can be played by the actor who plays Mum)

Elaine the Pain, social worker. A likeable, well-meaning bungler with little intuition and a lot of knowledge.

Mum, self-deceiving, unreliable, with poor impulse control. She never had a good mother to teach her how to be a good mother.

Cam, writer. Bookish, clever, steady. Spontaneous as long as she has a week's notice.

The following small roles can be doubled or can be cast individually:

Ted
Julie
Worm scene kids
Stan
Vi
Margaret
Mark
Justine's Dad
Lady Writer

MUSICAL NUMBERS

ACT I

No. 1	**Overture**	
No. 2	**Tracy Beaker's Back**	Tracy and Company
No. 3	**Hollywood Mum**	Tracy and Mum
No. 4	**Friends For Never**	Tracy and Justine
No. 5	**Tropical Sea**	Peter and Company
No. 6	**Wanted**	Tracy
No. 7	**Goodenuff For Me**	Peter, Stan and Vi
No. 8	**Once Upon A Time**	Justine
No. 9	**Someone I Could Trust**	Tracy

ACT II

No. 10	**Entr'acte**	
No. 11	**Something About Her**	Cam and Tracy
No. 12	**Waiting**	Justine and Tracy
No. 13	**Will She Still Want Me**	Cam, Tracy, Mum and Company
No. 14	**Eat My Dust**	Tracy and Mum
No. 15	**Waiting** reprise	Cam
No. 16	**Letting Her Grow**	Cam
No. 17	**Hollywood Mum** reprise	Tracy
No. 18	**Elaine the Pain**	Elaine and Kids
No. 19	**Finale**	Company
No. 20	**Playout**	

The vocal score and backing tracks are available on hire from Samuel French Ltd.

ACT I

SCENE 1

No. 1: Overture

The Dumping Ground

Kids are sitting peacefully in the Dumping Ground

*Elaine wheels a wheelie bin in. All watch. Cam follows the bin anxiously.
Teenage Tracy Beaker pops out of it like a Jack-in-the-Box, screaming
loudly*

Tracy (*amplified scream*) AAARRRGGGHHH!!!

Everyone watches, appalled, then —

All AAARRRGGGHHH!!! Tracy Beaker's back!

*Tracy chucks her belongings out of the bin, including a notebook with
her life story in it*

Kid She's back and she's baaaaad.

No. 2: Tracy Beaker's Back

Tracy
Once upon a time
There was a little girl
A sweet girl who
Through no fault of her own
Ended up in care
Ended up in strife
Wondering why she was left alone.

You might wonder why
A girl as nice as me
Should end up in this place of little care.
You might think I should have

              The best in life,
              Instead of being shunted here and there.

Justine That's why they call her "Boomerang Beaker"

All	And now it's all bad 'cos Beaker's back
Tracy	Things'll get more int'resting now Beaker's back in town
All	We're all mad, 'cos Beaker's back Bringing chaos to the dumping ground.

Cam Tracy ——
Tracy (*yelling at Cam*) I'll never speak to you again, Cam Lawson, and I'll never forgive you, you … dumper!
Cam That's not fair! I didn't dump you!

Tracy turns on Elaine

Tracy I see all the kids that were here when I left are still here, Elaine.
Elaine Um …
Tracy Bottom fallen out of the fostering market, has it?! Call yourself a social worker! (*She sings*)

              You will hear how I
              Can face the world alone
              With no one there to catch me when I fall.
              Surely you'll admire
              This heroine so fair
              Who bravely and with charm will conquer all.

All	And now we've lost hope 'cos Beaker's back.
Tracy	Back on top and ready to step in and take control.
All	It's like a soap 'cos Beaker's back Making sure she's got the starring role.

Peter tentatively approaches

Tracy What do you want, weed?
Peter Nothing.
Tracy (*to audience*) Peter Ingham, the boy who asked for nothing.
Peter I do ask. I just don't want as much as you.

Tracy's eyes fall on Justine

Justine Well, well, well, dumped again.
Peter Em, Cam didn't actually look like she was dumping Tracy, Justine.
Tracy What would you know about it, dripweed?! (*She turns to the audience*) She dumped me just like all my foster parents. It's the same old story! And I've got it all written down to prove it! (*She sings*)

> So when you hear my story,
> The story of my life,
> I know that I will have your sympathy
> So hankies ready, you'll feel so sad and sorry.

Justine Yeah, sorry you came.

Tracy   And wonder why the world did this to me.

All   And now all is bad 'cos Beaker's back.
Tracy   Right on form and ready to come through
                            'cos I'm so cool.
All   Hopping mad 'cos Beaker's back
Tracy   Back to putting up with all these fools
                            and all these rules.

All   Get on track 'cos Beaker's back
                     Stomping through the dumping ground
                            just like a ten ton truck.
                     Can't relax, 'cos Beaker's back
                     Out of love but not down on her luck.
                     It's all bad.
Tracy   It's not bad.
                     'Cos Tracy Beaker's back!

Justine Sure, it's all the world's fault.
Peter Tracy has been a bit unlucky in life, Justine.
Tracy Will you two stop wittering! (*To audience*) Ignore them, this is my story and I'm telling it my way. (*She opens her life story notebook*) Chapter One. We rewind the years to ——
Peter Technically, you can't rewind life, you haven't got a remote, for a start.
Tracy If you don't stop buzzing at me like a giant mosquito you won't be in the story!

Peter leaves

Chapter One. Ted and Julie, the cruel foster parents.

SCENE 2

The past

Ted and Julie appear. They are meek, vegetarian, sandals types. Julie is pregnant

Ted The thing is, Tracy, what with Julie having the baby and all ...
Tracy I can't wait! I'll bath it for you and take it for walks — you should see how fast I can run with a pram —

Julie tries not to panic

It will love having a big sister.
Ted We have to be straight with you, Tracy. Your social worker tells us you don't have much patience for babies.
Tracy That's a lie! I love babies! There was a baby in my last dumping ground and she loved me!
Julie Em, apparently, you shut her in a cupboard.
Tracy It was the airing cupboard! She was warm and comfy there.
Julie Nobody could hear her crying.
Tracy Der, that was the point!
Ted The point is, Tracy ...
Julie What Ted is trying to say, it's not that we don't care about you, but ...
Ted The baby will need our attention.
Tracy Babies can be very demanding.
Ted Then you understand?
Tracy Understand what?

A big silence

You're dumping me?
Julie Of course not, we'll keep in touch.
Ted Take you out on the weekends —
Tracy Don't bother! I never want to see you again!
Julie Tracy —
Tracy AAARRRGGGHHH!!!

SCENE 3

The past

Back in the Dumping Ground

Elaine I know you must be feeling angry and disappointed, Tracy …
Tracy I am, Elaine, very disappointed — in you.
Elaine Perhaps we could have a little chat about why all your fosterings
go wrong?
Tracy You're the one that sent me to Auntie Peggy Smack-Smack, Mr
and Mrs Slimy Stew and now Ted and Julie Chickpea have turned out
hopeless as well!
Elaine They still want to visit, to take you out. It's better than nothing.
Tracy No it's not, it's worse than nothing.
Elaine Oh, Tracy, I'm sorry. Here, let me ——

Elaine tries to wipe Tracy's eyes. Tracy bats her away angrily

Tracy Tracy Beaker doesn't cry! I've got hay fever!
Elaine If you say so.

Elaine exits

Tracy (*to the audience*) And as if that wasn't enough, little Tracy then
discovered the Dumping Ground had been invaded by aliens while she
was with Ted and Julie.

SCENE 4

The past

Justine enters and stares coldly at Tracy

Tracy Who are you!?

Justine doesn't answer

Let me put it another way. (*Shouting*) WHO ARE YOU?!!
Justine I ask the questions 'round here.
Tracy Really? Then ask yourself this, little cowpat. Do I really want to
cheek the Beaker? Well, do you?

Justine So this is the famous Tracy Beaker. I thought you'd be bigger.

Peter appears

Tracy doesn't see him. He sneezes

Peter Bless me.
Tracy Another one! Where did you come from?!
Peter Exeter.
Tracy Tragic. Are there any more new kids Elaine the Pain forgot to warn me about?
Peter Just me and her.
Tracy What's your name?
Peter (*tiny*) Peter Ingham.
Tracy Pardon?
Peter Peter Ingham. I, em, I have to ... (*He tries to escape*)

Tracy blocks Peter's escape. He is terrified

Tracy Temporary care or dumped for good?

Peter stares at her

Speak up.
Peter My nan died.
Tracy Parents?

Peter shakes his head

Dumped for good.
Peter Are you dumped for good?
Tracy Of course not!
Peter (*to Justine*) Are you?
Justine No! I'm only here for a few weeks.
Tracy That's what they all say.
Justine My dad had some bad luck, that's all. He's getting on his feet again and getting us a new house.
Peter How come you're here, Tracy?
Tracy None of your ——
Justine I heard it's because her mum dumped her when she was a baby.
Tracy That's a lie!

Tracy is on the spot. Peter and Justine wait

My mother ... is away.
Justine D'oh! Obviously!
Tracy Making Hollywood films!

Peter buys it

I've been there. To her mansion.
Peter She must be very rich.
Tracy (*at Justine*) D'oh, obviously! (*She sings*)

No. 3: Hollywood Mum

There's a place where dreams are made
Where the bright lights never fade,
And the stars are on parade
Each night.

Justine Yeah, planet fat chance.

Tracy   It's the place where I will go
With the one who loves me so
And together we will glow
So bright.
You are beautiful
My superstar
Lighting up the darkest night from where you are.

Mum enters

Peter (*seeing Mum*) Wow!

Mum   Adore me
Implore me
And I'll shine brighter still.
So snap me
Unwrap me
Your dreams I will fulfil.
I could have been a great scientist
But I'm just a wee bit dumb
But I know just how to be
A Hollywood mum.

Justine I've never heard of a star called Beaker.
Tracy Well obviously she's not going to use her real name.

Justine So when is she coming back for you?
Tracy Well, she is very busy and in demand.
Justine Sure she is. (Not).

Tracy   There's a place where she must stay
                              But she'll take me home one day
                              When the sky's no longer grey
                              She'll come.
                              Until then from way afar
                              She will shine, my superstar
                              Driving in her big pink car,
                              My mum.

                              While she shines on me
                              Life won't be bad.
                              Nothing else will worry me
                              I won't be sad.

Mum   Adore me
                              Implore me
                              And I'll shine brighter still.
                              So snap me
                              Unwrap me
                              Your dreams I will fulfil.
                              I could have been a great novelist
                              But how could I waste this bum
                              And I know just how to be
                              A Hollywood mum.

                              I am beautiful.
Tracy   You are beautiful.
Mum   Keep me in your light.
Tracy   Keep me in your light.
Mum   I am wonderful.
Tracy   You are wonderful.
Mum   And I've got absolutely no cellulite!

Tracy   Seeing her the way I've seen
                              Lighting up the movie screen
                              They will see my dream is true
                              Mum they will believe in you.
                              Then see how much they'll envy me
                              As away from here we run
                              And our lives will be such fun,

My Hollywood mum.
My Hollywood mum.
My Hollywood mum.

Justine So, all that and you live in a care home.
Peter Maybe she left Tracy here because she's filming in the jungle, Justine. It's no place for a child, the jungle.
Tracy Exactly. And she doesn't want me to miss school.
Justine Dream on, Tracy Beaker.
Tracy Remind me again — why did your dad dump you? Oh, yes, he's hopeless.

Louise appears

Louise Hi, Tracy.

Tracy is pleased to see Louise

Justine You were right, Louise, Tracy Beaker is the biggest liar in the world.
Tracy What?
Louise I didn't ... (*Say that*)
Tracy (*to Louise*) Who is this ... whatever it is?
Louise Justine Littlewood.
Peter She's Louise's best friend.
Tracy Wrong. I'm Louise's best friend.
Justine Wrong. You *were* Louise's best friend.
Louise Maybe we can all be friends.
Tracy Let me think about that for a minute. No. We're leaving, Louise. My room.

Tracy and Justine tug Louise in opposite directions

Justine She's going nowhere, she's with me.
Tracy I'm back and she's dumping you. Aren't you, Louise?
Louise I can't!
Tracy What?

Louise runs off, upset

Justine Told you.

Tracy launches herself on Justine

Elaine rushes on to separate them

Tracy "accidentally" kicks Elaine in the shin

Elaine Ow! (*She hops around*)

The company shouts very loudly, in unison

All QUIET ROOM!

SCENE 5

The past

Elaine and Tracy are in the Quiet Room. There's a bean bag on the floor

Tracy You have no right to imprison me!
Elaine Tracy, the Quiet Room is for calm thoughts and reflection on your behaviour. Let's just take a few deep breaths.

Elaine deep breathes on her own

Tracy So how's your love life, Elaine?
Elaine We both know that staff do not discuss their personal lives with the child — er, the clients. Over-familiarity could lead to more emotional damage.
Tracy Only, you're not getting any younger.
Elaine This is not about me, Tracy!
Tracy I was just being caring, Elaine.
Elaine I'm the social worker! I do the caring!

Elaine stomps off

Tracy is alone, and we see her vulnerability for a moment

Louise furtively enters

Tracy I knew you'd come!
Louise Shhh. I'll get in trouble.
Tracy I knew you'd dump her!
Louise I can't dump Justine.
Tracy What?

Louise She was really nice to me while you were with Julie and Ted.
Tracy But I'm back.
Louise I waited and waited for you to come and see me or phone me.
Tracy I was going to, honest.
Louise It was like you forgot all about me when you got fostered.
Tracy I was busy! I had family responsibilities! I nearly had a baby to look after!

Justine enters

What's she doing here?!
Louise She's got something to say to you.

Louise urges Justine to speak

Justine I'll try to be —
Louise Try hard ...

It nearly chokes Justine

Justine I'll try hard to be friends with you if you try too.
Tracy No way! (*She sings*)

No. 4: Friends for Never

> She thinks she can stroll in here
> Be all chummy so it seems.

Louise She was only trying to —

Tracy
> She'll soon find out my friendship
> Was only in her dreams!

Louise — be nice!

Justine
> She acts like she's the queen bee
> Making people walk the line.

Louise She's not so bad when —

Justine
> She is just the perfect person
> To NOT be a friend of mine!

Louise — you get to know her.

Tracy	She's mad, she's rude
	And I really think she should
	Go drown herself deep down in the cold blue sea.
Justine	She's hard as brick
	And she makes me feel quite sick
	And she'll never ever get well in with me!
Tracy	I'm not impressed now
Justine	She's self-obsessed now

Louise (*to both*) You drive me round the bend!

All	Let's all just be friends ...
Tracy **Justine**	} For NEVER!

Louise (*shrieking*) Stop it! Both of you!

Tracy and Justine stare at Louise for a moment, then resume in unison as if nothing happened

Justine	She couldn't be a mate of mine,
	I can't pretend.
Tracy	Let me make my thoughts about her quite clear.
Justine	A perfect day gets cold and grey
	When she descends.
Tracy	She's a special kind of pain in the rear.
Justine	She could be my greatest enemy
	Until my life ends.
Tracy	She's the girl that no one wants to be near.
Justine **Tracy**	} But friends?

Tracy Me?
Justine And her?

Tracy **Justine**	} NEVER!
	She's mean, she's bad
	And she must have gone quite mad
	If she thinks she could become a friend of mine.
	She thinks she's smart
	Hope to die and cross my heart
	And I'm gonna hate her till the end of time!

Tracy	This is my stance now
Justine	She's had her chance now
Tracy	
Justine	} So here our story ends
	Won't you be my friend
	For NEVER!

Louise Oh please, can't you even try — for me?

Tracy	} Won't you be my friend
Justine	For NEVER!

Louise But —

Tracy	} NEVER!
Justine	

Louise Then I just don't know what to do!
Tracy Well I do!

SCENE 6

The past

Kids, Peter, Tracy and Justine are on stage. Tracy and Justine are eyeballing again

Tracy The winner of the dare gets exclusive rights to Louise, right?
Justine The loser never gets to be her friend ever again, right?
Tracy Right. I dare you to climb to the top of the big tree.

Reaction from other kids

Justine Too easy.
Tracy I dare you to sneak into the attic and stay all night — without a torch.

Reaction from kids

Justine How weak is that?!
Tracy I dare you to put itching powder on the toilet seat.

Reaction from kids

Justine Oh, puh-lease.
Tracy Well, you name the dare if you're so smart!

A kid happens to be passing with a jar of worms

Justine First one to eat a worm wins.

Worm wrangling. Justine takes one. She holds it up and lowers it into her mouth. She swallows hard

And I think we have a winner.

Kids are amazed

Tracy I'll eat two!
Peter Eat them together, Tracy, it'll be easier. For you, I mean, not for the worms.
Tracy I don't need advice from a dandelion! (*She eats the worms with great difficulty. She convulses*) I win.
Justine holds her worm up — she had palmed it

Justine Sucker. Imagine being stupid enough to eat worms! What a baby!

They all run off except Tracy

Elaine runs in with a bucket

Tracy puts her head in it and we hear magnified heavings. Elaine is squeamish

Elaine There there.
Tracy It would be easier to let them travel the other way.
Elaine I have to see them safely out.

More heavings. Elaine looks in the bucket

And there they are.

Elaine almost faints and staggers out

Louise enters

Louise (*to Tracy*) How could you do such a thing?

Tracy I did it for you — we can both forget about Justine Littlewood now. I won the dare.
Louise You didn't win me! I'm not a cheap teddy bear in a fairground!
Tracy But she cheated.
Louise You just don't get it do you?!
Tracy Yeah, I get it. You'd rather be friends with her than me! Fine! I never want to speak to you again!

Louise exits

Peter comes on. He goes to Tracy, shy

Peter I'll be your friend, Tracy.

Tracy heaves particularly noisily into the bucket

You're welcome.

Tracy addresses the audience

Tracy See? Dumped again! And by soppy Louise of all people. How humiliating. And even more humiliating, I was landed with wet Peter Ingham to look after. Very wet Peter Ingham. Chapter "Man the Lifeboats!"

SCENE 7

The past. Night

Peter enters with a wet sheet, furtively looking for the laundry room. He has wet his bed. Tracy enters, creeping furtively to her room with stolen food. Peter and Tracy bump into each other and scream

Tracy Shhhh! What are you doing creeping around?!
Peter Just having a walk.
Tracy In the middle of the night?
Peter Nan always says, I mean, she always *said* a walk was good for helping you to sleep.
Tracy She was right, but most people take the dog with them, not their sheets.

Peter tries not to cry

All right, don't add more water to the situation.

Peter I don't know how it happened, I was having this beautiful dream. (*He sings*)

No. 5: Tropical Sea

I dreamt I swam in a tropical sea,
Floating and turning weightless and free
We dived to the bottom, my teddy and me,
In the tropical sea.

All I swam right down in the paradise bay,
Giggled as swordfish jumped through the spray,
I sang with the mermaids and stayed for a day,
In the tropical sea.
Slipping through soft arms of seaweed,
Adrift on the billowing waves.
A chattering dolphin followed my lead
And we teased timid creatures in peekaboo caves.
Down on the seabed, weightless and free,
Where darting bright fish come to play.
Bubbles rise like laughter tickling me,
And take all my worries away.

I dreamt I swam in a tropical sea
Floating and turning, weightless and free.
We dived to the bottom, my teddy and me
In the tropical sea.
I swam right down in the paradise bay,
Giggled as swordfish jumped through the spray,
I sang with the mermaids and stayed for a day
In the tropical sea.

A giant whale idling, its back is my bed
An octopus massage for free
A shark gliding by with its engine switched off
Eyeball to eyeball with me.

Then dolphins scattered like fighter planes,
And I woke in a panic to see,
The tropical ocean
Had turned cold as rain
And dived into bed with me.

Tracy Don't worry. It happens to everyone when they first come.
Peter It happened to you?
Tracy I meant everyone else!
Peter Sorry.
Tracy Well, don't stand there shivering, we'll put it (*the sheet*) in the washing basket.
Peter I want to wash it myself.
Tracy Don't be pathetic. The staff don't care, in fact they won't even mention it. Elaine the Pain says it's a syndrome, not a problem.
Peter I've got a syndrome?
Tracy I've got one too. Mine is aggressive compensatory behavioural problems.

Peter is very impressed

I've also got an attachment disorder.
Peter Wow!
Tracy Come on then, I'll show you where the clean sheets are.
Peter Tracy?
Tracy What now?
Peter You're my first friend in the care home.

Tracy grabs a handful of Peter's pyjamas

Tracy Number one, Dripweed, this place is not a care home, it's a don't-care home. That's why it's called the Dumping Ground. And number two — you are not — N.O.T. — not my friend!

Tracy stomps off

Peter That's just her syndrome talking.

Tracy enters in the present

Tracy (*to the audience*) So dear little Tracy was even more friendless and uncared for and she realized something desperate had to be done to solve her lack of fostering success — and let's face it, there's nothing more desperate than Elaine the Pain!

SCENE 8

The past

Tracy joins Elaine

Elaine I'm glad you requested a little session to work on your fostering issues, Tracy.

Tracy And I'm glad you realize you need to work on my fostering issues, Elaine!

Elaine Me?

Tracy No more excuses and blame-shifting. Just get out there and find the right foster parents for me.

Elaine Tracy, I don't think you fully appreciate the difficulties involved —

Tracy A bit more commitment might help!

Elaine I'm very committed to my job.

Tracy Just hopeless then.

Elaine tries to count to ten to calm herself but Tracy counts backwards to confound her

Elaine One, two, three …

Tracy Ten, nine, eight …

Elaine Tracy!

Tracy Anger management technique not working?

Elaine Sometimes you — this job can be very challenging!!

Tracy Why don't you foster me then —

Elaine NOOOOO! (*Beat*) I meant thank you very much, but I can't foster you.

Tracy It's not as if you have any kids — have you?

Elaine My private life is sacrosanct!

Tracy True, but it will get better with me around.

Elaine I meant it has to stay private!

Tracy Why?

Elaine We're not here to discuss me!

Tracy You're right. We're here to discuss you getting me foster parents who are prepared to give me everything.

Elaine Nobody gets everything. Life's not like that. Life is …

Tracy I know, Elaine, life is like a box of chocolates.

Elaine Em, it wasn't me that said that.

Tracy Except for care kids it's half a box of chocolates — that someone else has eaten all the best ones from!

Elaine Can't we just be grateful for the chocolates we do get?

Tracy No way! I want the heart-shaped, pink-ribboned, giant box of chocolates all to myself! So get with the programme and find me my Mr and Mrs Willy Wonka! (*To the audience*) Could I have been any clearer? Not even Elaine could fail to understand what she had to do. Could she?

SCENE 9

The past

Elaine now has a clipboard and pen

Elaine Tracy! You'll never guess!
Tracy You're right.

Tracy slopes off

Elaine Tracy! Come back! Honestly!
Tracy Well, spit it out, Elaine!
Elaine There's a lovely couple here, enquiring about fostering a little girl!
Tracy See what a little effort does?
Elaine Of course there will have to be checks and paperwork ...
Tracy (*sweet*) But first, Elaine ... (*Yelling*) Handcuff them before they get away!
Elaine Silly Billy.

Margaret and Mark, a stylish young couple, appear

Tracy I'll take it from here, Elaine.

Tracy grabs Elaine's clipboard and pen and shoves her off stage

Elaine goes

Tracy inspects the couple, ticking points on the clipboard

Margaret We've been so looking forward to this.
Mark Margaret really wants a little girl to dress and fuss over, don't you?
Margaret Absolutely.

Another tick

Tracy You won't mind a few questions, will you? The authorities don't want just anybody taking kids home.
Margaret Of course.
Tracy Home cooking or takeaway?
Margaret Home cooking. Nutrition is very important.

Bad news

Mark Except on weekdays and when we go abroad on holiday — you do like holidays abroad, I hope?

A big tick

Tracy TV in my room?
Margaret We don't bother much with TV.

Disappointment

Mark Because, we have a huge home cinema!
Margaret And Mark is mad for computer games.

Ecstasy. A huge tick

Tracy Of course I'd want a pet. Maybe two.
 Louise walks in

Margaret Oh, how lovely …

But she doesn't mean the pets. We hear beautiful music

Tracy Excuse me …

   Mark and Margaret take Louise by the hand and leave with her

(*To the audience*) And so, in spite of her superior intelligence and her engaging personality, poor little Tracy was left behind, sad and lonely as ever. But one day a miracle happened in the Dumping Ground. Elaine the Pain's three brain cells finally collided and she actually got a workable idea.

SCENE 10

The past

Elaine hurries in

Elaine (*calling*) Tracy! I've had a wonderful idea!
Tracy You're going to live in a hermit's cave in Outer Mongolia?
Elaine No, silly!
Tracy Pity.
Elaine I'll put an ad in the social services magazine!
Tracy Looking for another job won't get me fostered.
Elaine No, child of the week! I'll put your profile in the magazine.

Elaine exits

Tracy I'm going to have my very own advertisement. (*Dreamily*) With a picture of me looking adorable! (*To the audience*) I can look adorable! I am adorable! I'll be fostered in no time! (*She sings*)

No. 6: Wanted

Wanted, a dad.
Wanted, a mum.
Wanted, a place where all my friends could come.
It would be nice.
It would be fine.
If you would take me home and make your home
into a home of mine.

I'd have to change,
That's plain to see.
People would never want a kid like me.
I could be good.
I'd walk the line,
If you would take me home and make your home
into a home of mine.

I'd have to somehow find a way,
To hide all my rage and all my pain.
Then maybe I'd hear someone say
Tracy, let me take you home,
And make you mine,
For ever and a day.

Wanted, a life.
Wanted, some love.
Then I'd have everything
That I've dreamed of.
Somewhere to grow,
Somewhere to just be.
Someone to call my own.
Someone at home,
Who really wanted me.
Who really wanted me.

SCENE 11

The past

A kid comes running in clutching a magazine

Kid (*yelling*) Tracy Beaker is child of the week!

Tracy snatches the magazine off the kid and looks

Tracy (*yelling angrily*) Elaine!!

Elaine comes running

Elaine There better be a fire, Tracy!
Tracy What do you call this?! (*The magazine*)
Elaine You know very well it's the social services magazine.
Tracy How could you embarrass me like that!
Elaine What's wrong with it?
Tracy (*reading from the magazine*) "Tracy is a lively, healthy, chatty, eleven-year-old who has been in care for a number of years. Consequently she has a few behavioural problems!"
Elaine Rather nicely put, I thought.
Tracy (*reading*) "And needs *firm*, loving handling"?!
Elaine Well, it's not always in your best interests to let you get away with everything.
Tracy Why don't you just invite all the saddoes in the country round for a bit of happy slipper-slapping!
Elaine There's no point being dishonest with people.
Tracy There's every point! Rich people don't do firm loving handling and behavioural problems! They do fat pocket money and giant TVs

and spoiling people! Don't you know anything about marketing? It will be your fault if I end up here forever and ever!

SCENE 12

The present

Tracy And ever and ever ...
Justine At least you finally realized you just weren't foster-child material.
Tracy Well at least I've been fostered, unlike some people.
Justine Why would I want to be fostered? I'm going to live with my dad soon.
Tracy You should sell that story to the medical profession, it's been putting me to sleep for years.
Justine You're just jealous.
Tracy Sure I am. (*To the audience*) Chapter "Abandon All Hope": Justine Littlewood's dad.

We hear the doorbell bing-bonging

SCENE 13

The past

Justine is on stage

Justine's dad comes in carrying a plastic bag

Justine Daaaaaaaad! (*She launches herself at him*)
Dad Steady!
Justine I knew you'd come!
Dad Don't I always?
Justine It's been forever.
Dad I said I'd come when I could.
Justine How have you been?
Dad Life's hard on your own, you know.

Justine knows

   Mustn't complain, eh? Best foot forward. Soldier on.
Justine Yeah.
Dad Em, I can't stay long.

Justine What?
Dad Have to see a man about a job.
Justine But we were going out, you promised —
Dad Don't give your old man a hard time. Got enough on my plate.

Justine is gutted

(*Holding out the plastic bag*) I got you a present.

Justine takes the bag and pulls a Mickey Mouse clock from it

I remembered how much you liked Mickey Mouse.
Justine I love it.
Dad Honest?
Justine Honest.
Dad Now you've got something to remind you of your dad, eh?
Justine I really love it.
Dad Good. Well. Can't stand around. Give's a kiss.

Justine throws her arms round him

Let go.

She doesn't

Tell you what, next weekend we'll do the whole day out. All right?
Justine Promise?
Dad Promise. Let go.

Justine can't. He prises her arms from round his neck and she holds on to his waist. He prises her off and she slides down and holds his leg

Dad prises Justine off his leg and goes

Tracy enters

Tracy What's that?
Justine A present. My dad dropped in specially to give it to me.
Tracy Mickey Mouse, eh? It's been so long since you saw him he thinks you're still three.
Justine You're just jealous.
Tracy Of a stupid clock? It probably came from a charity shop.
Justine And where's all the presents from your famous mum? I mean, Hollywood does have a post office, doesn't it?!

Justine leaves

Tracy (*shouting*) Probably fall apart in minutes!

Tick tock sounds

A large Mickey Mouse clock on legs appears

Tracy furtively approaches it and plays with it, whizzing the arms round and round. They fall off. Tracy is sheepish

SCENE 14

The present

Tracy, Justine and Peter are on stage

Tracy (*to the audience*) Technically, I didn't break her clock. I was just winding it up and it … fell apart, all by itself.
Justine Everyone knew it was you.
Tracy I didn't break the clock!
Justine Did.
Tracy Didn't!
Justine Did!

They continue did and didn't-ing

Peter It's nice, this, though, isn't it? The three of us together again?
Justine Charming.
Peter I always think dumping ground kids are like the parcel in parcel parcel.
Tracy What goes on in that swamp you call a mind?
Peter Like, we're passed from hand to hand, but we always end up here, with all our protective wrappings peeled off. Just like parcel parcel.
Justine It's pass the parcel, you muffin.
Tracy It's muppet, you … muppet!
Peter Whatever. We still end up back here.
Tracy Serves you right for going off into the sunset with old-age pensioners. (*To the audience*) Chapter Pathetic. Peter Ingham and the ancient tribes.

SCENE 15

The past

Tracy blows a whistle

An elderly couple, Stan and Vi, appear. They jog and do push-ups etc. for Tracy

Peter approaches

Peter What are you doing to these people?
Tracy Getting them in shape in case I need them as back-up to foster me.
Peter You'll kill them, Tracy.
Tracy Exercise is good for you. Should have run your nan round the park a couple of times — she'd still be here now.
Peter (*to Stan and Vi*) Would you like a cup of tea?
Vi Oh, thank you, you're very kind.
Tracy No time, they're due for their spin class.
Peter They're tired, Tracy.
Tracy That's because they're out of shape.

Stan wheezes pathetically at Tracy

Oh all right, take five!

Tracy leaves

Stan and Vi make for the exit

Peter Don't go!
Stan We made a mistake.
Vi We're not up to fostering a child.
Peter Yes you are!
Stan Face it, son, we just don't make the grade.

No. 7: Goodenuff For Me

Peter   You don't have to be perfect
                     Or even the best you can be
                     You don't have to go set the world on fire,
                     Just listen to me.

> If Tracy's not the one then it is easy to see
> There's lots of other fishes in the deep blue sea.

Vi That's very nice of you, love.

Stan and Vi start to leave again

Peter Wait!
Vi Is there something else, pet?
Peter I don't like to …
Stan Spit it out, lad.
Peter Nan always said if you don't ask, you don't get.
Vi That's what I always say! Don't I, Stan?
Stan Aye.

Peter	Cups of tea by the fireside,
	Someone who's on your side,
	Telly on a weekend night with no school next day.
	It's OK ——
	And wouldn't a boy be easier?
Stan }	Fish and chips on a Friday night
Vi	Someone to hold me tight
	Someone who will want to stay.

Peter (*singing*) I don't need a lot, no need to worry …

| **Stan** } | And maybe he is right |
| **Vi** | Maybe it's all right. |

Peter Maybe it's all right. All right.

| **Stan** } | Could it be that he's the one we need? |
| **Vi** | Could it be that he is just the one we need? |

Stan What do you think love?
Vi He's got lovely manners.

Peter	Maybe you could take me to the seaside
	If you'd be so kind.
Stan }	Maybe we could take him to the seaside
Vi	If he wouldn't mind.
	And maybe we could love him just a little, little …

| **Peter** | And maybe you could love me just a little |
| **All** | If it's not too much to ask. |

Tracy enters

She sees Stan and Vi take Peter home

SCENE 16

The present

Tracy and Peter are on stage

Tracy (*to the audience*) See? Even foster parents past their sell-by date dumped me for drippy Peter Ingham. But it wasn't long before he was binned again too.

Peter hears her

Peter It wasn't Uncle Stan's fault his ticker gave out. And Auntie Vi visits me every Sunday.
Tracy (*to Peter*) You've got to learn to ask for more, Oliver.
Peter Huh?
Tracy Go back to the ant farm, I'm busy. (*To the audience*) Next chapter. Poor little Tracy ——

Peter is still watching Tracy. She sees

What are you staring at, Bug-eyes?
Peter Cut to the chase, Tracy.
Tracy What?
Peter That's what they say when people tell a story and never get to the important bit.
Tracy What important bit?
Peter (*to the audience*) Chapter "Opportunity Knocks". Tracy and the very special visitor.
Tracy Excuse me, who's telling this story?!

But the scene starts anyway

SCENE 17

The past

Elaine, Tracy, Justine and Kids are on stage

Elaine We have a very special visitor coming to see us! She's a writer!
Tracy Is she famous?
Elaine Oh, Tracy, that's not what's important.
Tracy She is famous!
Elaine Maybe she'll give us some tips on writing stories. Wouldn't that be nice?
Justine Why would a famous writer want to come to this dump?
Elaine She saw my child of the week segment in our magazine.
Tracy The one about me?!
Elaine I think she wants to write something about us all.
Tracy A famous lady writer is coming to see me?!

Grand music takes Tracy off to fantasy

Elaine Tracy?

SCENE 18

Tracy fantasy

A Lady Writer (Jacqueline Wilson clone) on a gilt chair floats in writing prettily in a large notebook. Tracy runs up to her

Lady Writer Oh, what a lovely child.
Tracy I can help you write your story, if you like. I'd only take half the money.
Lady Writer I'd be so grateful, I've got the most terrible writer's block.
Tracy But my name will have to be on the cover.
Lady Writer Of course. What is your name, dear?
Tracy Tracy Beaker.
Lady Writer Beautiful. The story of Tracy Beaker. You must come home with me at once. Don't bother packing, I'll have designers round to make you a whole new wardrobe. (*Calling off*) Bring the limousine, Tracy and I are going home.

Lady Writer is wheeled out again

Elaine Tracy, are you all right?

The music stops. End of fantasy

Tracy I'm fantastic, Elaine!
Elaine Oh, good.

Tracy panics

Tracy But I can't let a famous lady writer see me like this!
Elaine I don't think she'll be worried about what we're wearing.
Tracy Haven't you learned anything, Elaine?! It's the cute kids that get
fostered first!

Tracy tears off

Elaine sees Cam coming (we don't yet)

Elaine Oh, here she is! Children, Ms Cam Lawson, our very own
writer!

Grand fantasy music again

   Cam enters

Music grinds to a halt and all deflate. She's very ordinary

Cam Em, hi.

Elaine hands out notebooks and pencils

Elaine Now, I want you all to do your best work for Ms Lawson.
Cam I'd like to be called Cam, if that's OK.
Elaine (*to the kids*) Nice neat stories for Ms Cam. Maybe we'll put the
best ones in next month's social services magazine.
Cam Oh, no, there won't be best ones.
Elaine You'd be surprised. Some of our children have very good
imaginations.
Cam Sorry, I didn't mean that, I mean, it's creative writing … not a
competition. All of them would have to go in the magazine.
Elaine Oh.

The kids cluster around her, interested now

Cam It's not like school, just write whatever comes into your head. Anything at all.

Elaine leaves

Kids start writing

Peter Once upon a time there was a very handsome prince called Peter who had a kind grandmother ——
Cam Mmmm.

We hear beautiful music

    Tracy enters in a frilly dress, her hair tortured with slides and bows

The kids stare in amazement

Peter You look very nice, Tracy.
Justine Just like a film star — in a horror movie!

No. 8: Once Upon A Time

    (*Singing*) Once upon a time,
    There was a little girl,
    A lonely girl as pretty
    As could be.

Cam Lovely, em, Justine, is it?

Justine   Once upon one day
    A famous writer came
    And said, "Dear little girl
    Come home with me."

Peter Don't, Justine.

Justine   But when the famous writer
    Got this angel home
    They both found things were not
    Quite as they seem.

Cam Em, perhaps you should try a poem?

Justine   The famous writer
                       Wasn't very famous
                       And the pretty girl
                       A nightmare NOT a dream!

Cam gets very nervous as Justine taunts Tracy with the song lyrics

Tracy launches herself at Justine. Cam acts as if a swarm of ferrets were at her feet

Cam Please stop.

   Elaine runs in to try and separate them

Tracy kicks Elaine's shin

Elaine Ow!
All Quiet Room!

                              SCENE 19

The past. The Quiet Room

Tracy is far from quiet. Elaine nervously thrusts a foam rubber therapy bat at her to get it out of her system

Tracy belts the beanbag, the floor, herself, anything. Elaine backs away

Tracy I hate Justine Littlewood! I hate the Dumping Ground! I hate the Quiet Room!

   Cam appears

Tracy doesn't notice

Cam Tracy?
Tracy I hate Elaine the Pain! I hate stupid lady writers! I hate Tracy Beaker!
Cam Tracy!

No response

Elaine (*shouting operatically*) TRAAAAAAAAC-EY!

Tracy stops dead. She and Cam gape at Elaine. Even she didn't know she could do that

I'll leave you to have a little chat.

Elaine exits

Cam I'm sorry I'm not a famous writer.
Tracy So you should be! You're a big disappointment.
Cam That's what my mum always says.
Tracy Really? I thought people like you had mums who read them stories at bedtime and sent them to poncy schools.
Cam Yeah, I had those things.
Tracy Then you should be grateful, you got the whole box of chocolates.
Cam Unfortunately they were all hard centres.

Tracy is delighted that Cam "gets" it

Tracy Or chocolate covered ginger!
Cam Or those dark ones with the runny stuff and the chewy cherry inside!
Cam
Tracy } (*together*) Eeeugh!
Cam I came to bring you something.
Tracy A present?! For me?

Cam hands Tracy a notebook

A school notebook?! You really are a big disappointment!
Cam If you ever feel like writing it down, I'd love to read it. My address is inside.

Cam exits

Tracy (*shouting after her*) Don't you know giving a care kid personal details could lead to more emotional damage?! (*She opens the book, looking for the address. She finds it*) That's one very weird unfamous writer.

No. 9: Someone I Could Trust

(*Singing*) She gets my jokes and seems to understand
                    the things I say
She talks to me like she has got me sussed.
She's seen me at my worst and yet
                    she doesn't run away
She acts as if I'm someone she could trust!

Maybe there's a way that I could learn
                    to trust her too.
And ask her to become my one true friend.
Say to her quite clearly,
"Lady, all I need from you,
Is to stand by me until the very end."

Could I take the risk?
Could I take the chance?
Is she handing me on a gilded plate
An invitation to the dance?
This is something new
How should I adjust?
Is it something I can trust?

If I write things down for her
And tell her what's inside
Tell it like it is, keeping it true
Will it scare her off and make her
                    want to turn and hide?
Will she run away like others do?

In the very best of worlds
Where nothing can go wrong
Maybe she would stick to me like glue
And in time I'd learn to show her
                    all that's in my heart
Maybe I could learn to trust her too.

Could I take the risk?
Or are we poles apart?
Is she handing me on a gilded plate
An invitation to her heart?
How should I react?

Say that I'm not fussed?
When she's someone I could trust.

I don't have the time
Just to wait and see
So I will send to her on a gilded plate
An invitation to love me.
Then if she replies
And she surely must then
She's someone I could trust.

I'll write to her and make her see
If only she'll believe in me
I'll be the best that I can be for
Someone I could trust.

CURTAIN

ACT II

Scene 1

The present

Tracy has fallen asleep in a bean bag

No. 10: Entr'acte

Peter enters, dancing, unaware of Tracy's presence. He is very unhip and gawky, but abandoned, thinking he is alone. The music gets louder and wakes Tracy. She makes a "cut the music" gesture. It stops

Tracy (*to Peter*) If you go right now, I'll pretend I was just having a nightmare about mad stick insects taking over the Dumping Ground.

Peter hovers, all casual

Peter So, how's it going?
Tracy Any way you like, as long as you keep going!
Peter You know, I bet there's a little bit of tough old Tracy Beaker deep inside that's hurting just a teeny bit?
Tracy Have you been taking Elaine the Pain pills?
Peter I was just thinking …
Tracy Is that what the noise is?
Peter (*persevering bravely*) Why don't you give Cam a ring?
Tracy No way! She dumped me, remember.
Peter But you always make up.
Tracy Mind your beeswax, you … bee.
Peter Must have been something big this time.
Tracy Buzz buzzzzzzz buzzzzzzzzz!

Peter leaves, hurt

(*To the audience*) If she cared, she would have rung me by now. Wouldn't she? (*Beat*) But back to the story of me. Tracy is sick of everyone getting it wrong so she decides to take matters into her own hands. Chapter "What Were You Thinking." Tracy contacts the lady writer.

SCENE 2

The past

Cam and Tracy are on stage. Cam reads a letter from Tracy

Cam "Dear fellow lady writer, Tracy Beaker here. Enclosed is my story about Goblinda, the wicked fairy who flies around gobbing down on all the stupid wet fairies. I am also writing my autobiography, which, in case you don't know, is what your own story is called. By the way, if you want to become famous, you really should stop buying your jeans at Tesco." (*Amused*) Cheek! (*She sings*)

No. 11: Something About Her

I don't understand the way she gets right to me.
No one ever could be less like me.
But my lonely heart can't help but reach out to her
Knowing it was meant to be.

Tracy   She is not the kind of person I have dreamed of
She's not rich or cool as you'd expect.
But the funny way she smiled
        and saw right through me
Makes me hope against all hope we could connect.

Cam   There's something about her.
Something that is wild and free.
There's something about her,
Makes me think that maybe she could be
Mine alone, my one and only one for me.

Tracy   There's something about her
Something leads my heart astray.
There's something about her,
She's the one who'll take my pain away.

Cam
Tracy   } Someone tell me please, how I can
            Make her stay.

SCENE 3

The past. The Dumping Ground

Kids, Tracy and Justine are on stage

Elaine rushes in, excited

Elaine Tracy, wonderful news.
Justine Her mother ship came back for her?
Elaine (*to Tracy*) Someone is coming to see you!
Tracy I'm not going out with anyone else who's read about me in your sad magazine.
Elaine No, someone really, really, special to you.

Tracy is interested now

Tracy Who?
Elaine You'll never guess.
Tracy OK.
Elaine Tracy, I don't think you realize who this is. Someone who, frankly, I didn't think we'd ever see again.
Tracy MY MUM'S HERE!
Elaine Tracy, wait ——

Tracy runs off

Justine It's not her mum, is it?
Elaine I didn't mean — I mean, I didn't realize …

Elaine runs off

Justine They don't call her Elaine the Pain for nothing.

A beat, then Justine puts her fingers in her ears

Tracy screams the Tracy Beaker scream (off). This is followed by dishes crashing followed by:

Elaine (*from off*) Ow!
All QUIET ROOM!

SCENE 4

The past

Tracy is huddled on the Quiet Room bean bag. Cam comes in

Cam It's only me.

Tracy doesn't answer

We must stop meeting like this.
Tracy Ha-ha.
Cam Elaine told me what happened.

Tracy ignores her

I'm sorry I'm not your mum, Tracy.
Tracy Don't be stupid, how can my mum come, she's shooting three films a year.
Cam Mmmm.
Tracy Don't you believe me?
Cam It doesn't matter what I believe. Do you believe it?
Tracy You're here 'cos you think I'm going to help you write a soppy article about care kids.
Cam No. I'm here because I find you interesting.
Tracy Why?
Cam I don't know. Maybe it's because you're naughty. I was never brave enough to be naughty.
Tracy One. I'm not interesting, I'm fascinating. And two. I'm not naughty, I've got behavioural problems because of my tragic past.

Cam is amused

Cam Tracy ... I know this is mad, but ... how would you like to come out with me on Saturday?
Tracy To a posh restaurant?!
Cam I don't have money for posh restaurants. Maybe a free read in the bookshop and a cup of tea?
Tracy Puhlease! Do I look like Peter Ingham?
Cam I guess I could stretch to a burger.
Tracy Eleven. Don't be late.

SCENE 5

The past

Justine is waiting and watching for her dad

Tracy watches Justine from the present

Tracy (*in the present; to the audience*) Oh dear, Justine Littlewood's favourite weekend occupation. Clock watching for her Mickey Mouse dad.

Tracy joins Justine in the past

  Elaine is passing through

Justine (*to Elaine*) What time is it?
Elaine Eleven. He said ten, did he?
Justine He must have meant eleven.
Tracy (*to Justine*) Shove over, I want to watch for Cam coming. Did I mention she's taking me for a very nice lunch?
Justine I was here first.
Tracy (*to Elaine*) I'll probably be home late this evening. Cam and I have a lot to discuss.
Elaine Tracy, you weren't thinking of asking her to foster you? You really ought to get to know her first.

  Elaine exits

Justine Nah, grab her while you can. She'll drop you if she gets to know you.
Tracy If she does, I'll come back and wait here with you, for your dad. It will only be forever.
Justine Anyway, she's late. Probably won't turn up.

Tracy tries to hide the fear that Justine may be right. Justine sings

No. 12: Waiting

Justine   People say that I will find life waiting for me,
                           One day when the sun comes out again.
                           But for me the clouds roll by too slowly.
                           Waiting, waiting, all I see is rain.

It's all right
I don't mind.
There's nothing else I want to do.
So I might
Spend my time
Counting off the minutes while I'm waiting
For you.

Tracy   People say my dreams are way too big for me
So I tell them they don't know a thing
'Cos my dreams are mine alone and one day
I will see my dreams take wing.

I'm all right
I can wait.
There's nothing else I have to do.
So I might
Spend my time
Counting off the minutes while I'm waiting
For you.

Justine   People rushing by me they've got places to go
Always in a rush from here to there.
They don't stop to think, they just
                    keep up with the flow
Running past me unaware.

Tracy   Someone tell me why me?
Why am I the one who's always waiting here while
Life keeps passing by me
Why does no one seem to care?

Justine   ⎫
Tracy   ⎬ We're all right
              ⎭ We can wait
There's nothing else we have to do.
Might as well
Spend the time
Waiting 'til our dreams come true
Counting off the minutes while we're waiting
For you.

The doorbell rings

Tracy It's her!

Tracy runs out

Justine Maybe he said twelve.

SCENE 6

The past. A burger bar

During this scene we see Justine is still waiting for her dad. Cam and Tracy are at a table

Cam How could you eat all that?
Tracy It might be weeks before I see junk food again. I saw Elaine with some five-portions-a-day posters.
Cam You'll need five tons of fruit and veg to make up for that lot!
Tracy Don't worry. I won't eat this much when you foster me.
Cam Foster you? Where did you get that idea?!
Tracy I don't have to move in straight away, it will take Elaine a while to do the checks and the paperwork.
Cam Tracy, I'm a single woman —
Tracy The authorities don't care about that any more.
Cam — and I want to stay that way for now. No partner, no children.
Tracy That would be best. I don't have the patience for babies. It's in my file.
Cam You're impossible!
Tracy But you'll think about it?
Cam I've just told you —
Tracy It's not much to ask, just thinking about it.
Cam OK, I'll think about it, just to stop you nagging.
Tracy Well, you'd better buy me some presents to keep me going until you make up your mind.
Cam I'm a struggling writer, remember?
Tracy They pay people heaps for fostering. I could be your main source of income for years.
Cam Tracy —
Tracy Surely that's worth a teeny present?

Cam digs in her bag and brings out a Mickey Mouse pen

Cam Here, it's my lucky pen. You can have it.

Tracy Mickey Mouse — that's so cute! Justine Littlewood will eat her arm off with jealousy.

Cam It's only a pen.

Tracy This pen is going to be worth a fortune when its owner is famous!

Cam I doubt I'll ever be famous.

Tracy But I will! I'll write my tragic life story with it and Hollywood producers will fight over the rights! I love it!

Tracy hugs Cam tight. Cam hugs back. When Cam thinks the hug is over she finds Tracy still clinging. She hugs her some more, tenderly

SCENE 7

The past. The Dumping Ground

Justine is still waiting for her dad

Tracy returns. She stops dead when she sees Justine

Justine Go on, gloat. Get it over with.

Tracy walks up to her

Tracy I'm sorry he didn't come. And I'm sorry *someone* broke your stupid clock.

Justine Leave me alone.

Tracy holds out the pen and wiggles it. It looks like she's taunting

Tracy Look what Cam gave me. You love Mickey Mouse, don't you?

Justine is too gutted to fight

   Tracy gently puts the pen in Justine's hand and walks away

SCENE 8

The present

Tracy (*to the audience*) Tracy received nothing but ingratitude for her incredible generosity — and also had to write with cheap biros instead of a famous pen!

Peter enters

Anyway, the lady writer agreed to foster little Tracy and they lived happily ever after.
Peter If they lived happily ever after you wouldn't be back here, would you?
Tracy You have to give stories a happy ending.
Peter Yes, when it's finished. Nan always said finish what you started.
Tracy She should never have pushed *your* start button.
Peter Tracy and Cam ...
Tracy All right! Tracy and Cam got together ... for a few months and split up ... for a few months and got back together for a few months ——
Peter Fast forward, Tracy, they won't want the boring bits ... (*He points in her life book*) 'Til one day ... (*to audience*) Cam asked Tracy a very important question.

SCENE 9

The recent past

Cam and Tracy are on stage. Though we are still in the past, Tracy is now older

Cam Tracy, there's a very important question I need to ask you.
Tracy We're not renting *Bridget Jones* again.
Cam No, something really important.
Tracy What?
Cam It's been ages since you went back to the care home, hasn't it?
Tracy (*in dismay*)You're sick of me!
Cam No! Of course not! It's just — we've been together quite a while this time.
Tracy So?
Cam Well ... I'll never get used to having my life turned upside down, but we rub along all right these days, don't we?
Tracy That's 'cos you've finally learned who's boss.

Cam Be serious.
Tracy I am.
Cam Tracy … how would you like me to adopt you?

Tracy can't believe her ears

Tracy Say that again.
Cam I'd like to adopt you.
Tracy Again.
Cam I want to adopt you.

Tracy has a rapid fantasy:

A large, pink-ribboned, heart-shaped box of chocolates on legs appears on stage

Tracy hugs it, dances around with it for a few ecstatic moments

Tracy (*to Cam*) You want to be my …

The phone rings. Tracy picks it up, zombie-like

Hello?

Tracy is still staring at Cam, who is anxiously staring back

Mum?
Cam You wouldn't have to call me that — unless you want to.
Tracy My mum?

Cam takes the phone from Tracy

Cam (*into the phone*) We'll call you back. (*She hangs up the phone*)
    Yes, your mum. I'd like to be your mum.
Tracy That was Elaine. My real mum's come back.

Scene 10

The past

Cam is putting a locket or charm round Tracy's neck. Tracy is very nervous

Cam It's for luck. Hold on to it if you get nervous.
Tracy I have to look nice for her.
Cam You look beautiful.
Tracy I wonder what she'll look like?
Cam Don't you remember her?
Tracy Of course I do — it hasn't been that long!
Cam Tracy.
Tracy What?
Cam Don't pin all your hopes on her. She did leave you.
Tracy She came back. Why would she come back if she didn't want me? (*She sings*)

No. 13: Will She Still Want Me?

If she smiles when she first sees me
If she hurries through the door
If it looks like it was always meant to be
If I say that I'll be better
Than I ever was before
Then will she still want me?

Cam
If she finds the one who loved her
If her dreams can all come true
Making ev'rything the way that it should be
If her life can now be happy
Without what I have to give
Then will she still want me?

Tracy
Cam
} If I ask for way too much
Then it's only 'cos I'm scared
That she will see straight through the heart of me.
If I state my case too clear
Will I lose her from my life
And questions come around
Like will she still want me?

Mum appears for the first time

Mum   All this time I've spent believing
                      Through the years I've been away
                      What I needed most of all was to be free
                      Will this meeting be the answer
                      To the emptiness inside
                      And will she still want me?

                      If I seem to run away
                      It is just because I fear
                      That she will see straight through the heart of me
                      If she needs more than I have
                      Will I let her down once more?
                      Then what will be will be
                      And will she still want me?

All   If I ask for way too much,
                      Then it's only 'cos I'm scared
                      That she will see straight through the heart of me
                      If I state my case too clear
                      Will I lose her from my life?
                      And questions come around
                      Questions come around.

Mum
Tracy   } *(together; singing)* Like will she still want me?
Cam

SCENE 11

The past

Elaine is waiting to pounce on Mum and Tracy as they leave

Elaine I wanted to have a word before you and Tracy go out.
Mum Excuse me?
Tracy Elaine, we don't have time for a little session now!
Elaine Just a few minutes, Tracy.
Mum I'm sorry, um, Irene, is it?
Elaine Elaine. Tracy's social worker. We talked on the —— *(telephone)*
Mum And what was it, exactly, Ailene, that you wanted to say?
Elaine Well, um … I … It's just, it's been a long time, you two don't

really know each other and ideally we'd all have a little ... session, just so we're ——
Tracy Excuse me! Is that my life going past while you rabbit on?
Mum I think my daughter and I can manage, but thank you for your interest.

Mum and Tracy walk away

Elaine (*calling after them*) You do have an attachment disorder to overcome!

SCENE 12

The present

Tracy and Peter are on stage

Tracy There. Tracy and her mum lived happily ever after.
Peter Ahem.
Tracy Who asked you?
Peter I'm only saying ...
Tracy I *was* happy, my mum was back and there were presents and treats and ... and ... more presents! (*She is beginning to feel uncomfortable about the story*)

SCENE 13

The past. Mum's place

Tracy and Mum are on stage. Tracy sees a present

Tracy Is this for me?!
Mum No it's for the other Tracy in my life. Well, aren't you going to open it?

Tracy opens it and reveals a small fairy outfit

Oops, didn't realize how big you've got ...
Tracy It's really pretty.
Mum You probably don't even like fairies any more.
Tracy I do! I write these great stories, about a fairy called Goblinda. Goblin-da, get it?

Mum At least they didn't squash the imagination out of you in that place.
Tracy She has black wings and cross-eyes and she gobs on all the other fairies from a great height.
Mum Hope she gobs on that social worker person!!

Mum tweaks at Tracy's hair

We'll have to get that hair sorted.

Tracy hugs her and breathes her in

Tracy You smell nice, I remember your smell.
Mum Funny thing to say.
Tracy I love you.
Mum I love you too, darling.

Mum breaks the hug a shade too quickly

SCENE 14

The past

Tracy comes to Cam, excited

Tracy It was great! My mum's fabulous.
Cam Good! I'm pleased.
Tracy You should see her flat — well it's a bit small, but she's made it look amazing — just like in a magazine.
Cam People don't live in magazines.
Tracy What's that supposed to mean?
Cam Nothing, I'm sorry.
Tracy We stayed up until after midnight.
Cam On a school night?
Tracy We talked for hours.
Cam Good. What about?
Tracy You know, mother and daughter stuff.
Cam Oh.
Tracy You don't sound like you think it's good.
Cam Did she mention why she hadn't been to see you for so long?
Tracy You know why.
Cam I do?

Tracy Actresses have to be all over the place, at a moment's notice, it's no life for a child.
Cam Oh, Tracy ...
Tracy You should see all the things she bought me. And it's not even my birthday!
Cam A lot of birthdays went by without a word from her.
Tracy Why are you getting at my mum? She loves me!

Scene 15

The present

Tracy Obviously the lady writer was feeling very jealous and insecure. Can't blame her really ——
Peter Tracy ... It's OK if you wanted to talk to a friend (*me*) about, you know ...
Tracy My private life is sacrosanct.
Peter I just thought ...
Tracy That must have hurt.

Peter looks like he's going to snap back, but he leaves

Elaine enters. As Peter brushes past her she notices his anger

Elaine (*to Tracy*) What's going on?
Tracy Peter and I just had a little cognitive behaviour therapy session.
Elaine I think it would be better if you have your therapy sessions with an expert — someone outstanding in the field.
Tracy OK. Where's the field and who's this expert out standing in it?
Elaine Me, Tracy!

Elaine hears surreal cows in the field

Elaine hurries off

Scene 16

The past. Mum's place

Tracy is watching Mum putting lipstick on. Mum puts some on Tracy

Mum I'll get you some, maybe a lighter shade.
Tracy I love being with you!
Mum Me too, sweetheart.
Tracy I could stay a bit longer than the weekend. Cam wouldn't mind.
Mum Excuse me?
Tracy She's happy we're together again.
Mum Oh, is she? How nice of her.
Tracy Everyone is, Elaine and ——
Mum Since when did we care what they think?
Tracy It's just ——
Mum Aren't you forgetting something?
Tracy What?
Mum Who do we call on when these people interfere in our lives?

Tracy gets it. They shout

Tracy
Mum } (*together*) Goblinda!
Mum Spit in their eye! (*She sings*)

No. 14: Eat My Dust

When the world is hard and full of strife,
Nothing's ever given for free
You must grab all that you can from life
That's the lesson you can take from me.
You can even walk through fire
If you learn this simple key
Just give it a shot
And you can be hot.

I just
Spit in their eye,
Turn on my heel,
Show 'em the door
Keeping it real and say
Talk to the booty
'Cos the face ain't list'ning.

      Spit in their eye,
      Tell 'em I must
      Step on the gas
      And make them eat my dust
      And watch me walk away.

      When I feel the turkeys grind me down
      I flush them down the nearest drain
      I make sure that I don't hang around
      To let them do it to me once again.

      I have to be free! I have to be me!
      If you fail to see I am all I can be then …

(*Speaking, searching for a line*) Then … then …

Tracy (*speaking*) Go climb a tree!

Mum   Then go climb a tree!
      If you want a piece of good advice
      When they try to give you grief and pain
      Just say take a good look at this face
      'Cos you won't be seeing it again.

Mum
Tracy   } Spit in their eye,
Mum   Turn on my heel
      Show 'em the door

Mum
Tracy   } Keeping it real and say
      Talk to the booty
      'Cos the face ain't list'ning.
      Spit in their eye,

Mum   Tell 'em I must
      Step on the gas

Mum
Tracy   } And make them eat my dust
Mum   And watch me walk away.
      Hear me say it
      Eat my dust and watch me walk away.
Don't you let those so-called care workers shove you around. You're
a free spirit. Like me.
Tracy I won't.
Mum Remember, it was people like that who took you away from me.
Tracy I'm sorry, Mum.

Mum They hurt me very badly. I was barely more than a child myself. A baby with a baby. They were no help.

Tracy comforts Mum

Well, it's no use crying over spilt milk.
Tracy Or missing chocolates.
Mum Huh?
Tracy Never mind. I'll never leave you again. I promise.
Mum You're a funny thing …
Tracy I'll have to change schools.
Mum What?
Tracy Or I could get the bus, I don't mind, really.
Mum Um …
Tracy When I come to live.

Silence

Mum We'll have to talk about that. I'm late.
Tracy Are you going out again?
Mum Is that a tone in your voice?
Tracy No.
Mum Good.
Tracy Cam — I mean people take kids to the beer garden, outside, where kids are allowed.
Mum I can't take you this time. Surely I'm allowed the occasional night off?
Tracy I'll be fine.
Mum I won't be late.

Mum leaves

Tracy waits then sleeps

Cam is in her space

No. 15: Waiting Reprise

Cam   While she's gone I wait and stand by helplessly
                        I should go right back to being free
                        But I know I'll just keep right on waiting
                        Waiting, waiting,
                        'Til she's home with me.
                        It's all right, I don't mind

> There's nothing else I want to do
> So I might spend my time
> Counting off the hours while I'm waiting for you.

Scene 17

The past

Mum is sleeping. Tracy is gazing at her, willing her awake. She wakes, hungover

Mum Oh God. Why are you staring at me?
Tracy Did you have a good time?
Mum Mmmm.
Tracy Can we talk about it now?
Mum What?
Tracy About us being together forever.
Mum Get me some coffee, there's a love.
Tracy Then we can go and get my things.
Mum I might have to go away.
Tracy Away?
Mum For the weekend.
Tracy Why?
Mum Work. I can't get out of it.
Tracy But you don't have a job.
Mum I met someone who can get me a job! It's an opportunity I can't turn down.
Tracy Can we drive there?
Mum Um, I can't take you with me. You can stay here if you like.
Tracy On my own?
Mum You're not a baby, Tracy.
Tracy But all weekend ——
Mum Don't nag, sweetheart, I've got a headache.
Tracy I'll get you some aspirin.
Mum Maybe you'd better pop back to that Cam woman's a bit earlier.
Tracy But why? It's our weekend.
Mum You have no right to interrogate me! (*Beat*) I'm sorry, I'm just not used to sharing my space all the time.
Tracy Just tell me what I'm doing wrong and I'll stop.
Mum Pack up your things, there's a good girl. You can come again next weekend.

Mum exits

SCENE 18

The past

Tracy is in Cam's space

During this scene, Mum enters her space and places a present for Tracy

Cam You look tired. Is your mum making sure you get enough sleep?
Tracy I'm not a baby. I can go to bed when I choose.
Cam It's just when you get overtired, you ——
Tracy My mum treats me like an adult. Unlike some people.
Cam Things are still going well then?
Tracy Of course, why wouldn't they be?
Cam Are you sure?
Tracy I said, didn't I?!
Cam Good. I'm glad.
Tracy You're glad?
Cam You should get to know your real mum.
Tracy What if she wants me back? Would that make you "glad"?
Cam Does she want you back?
Tracy You'd get your stupid life right way round again! That's what you want, isn't it?
Cam Why are you saying these things?
Tracy I'm just telling you how much my mum wants me.
Cam Just ask me if there's something you need from me.
Tracy Don't you understand? She wants me back! (*Silence*) Say something!
Cam If your mum wants you back I'm very happy for you — if that's what you truly want.

Cam turns and walks away to hide her emotion

Tracy's voice is so small that Cam doesn't hear it

Tracy Fight for me.

No. 16: Letting Her Grow

Cam   Letting her grow,
                 Watching her hurting and sad.
                 Letting her be,
                 Knowing that I could be glad

If I knew that she
When she's far from me
Could somehow be happy.

Letting her grow
Letting her make her mistakes.
Hoping that she
Will always give more than she takes.
She will be missed
But I must assist
In making her happy.
Like a mother tiger
I'd fight tooth and nail
To keep her beside me
And not let her fail.
If I don't approve
I must not let it show,
It's all part of letting her grow.

Letting her grow
Telling her she'll be OK.
Letting her run
Before she can walk all the way.
Watching her fall
Then stand straight and tall
Is making me happy.

Like a mother eagle
Watch baby's first flight,
Nothing now can stop her soar
Out of my sight.
And I'd fight to hold her
But somehow I know
It's all part of letting her grow.

Like a mother swan
I can see how she'll bloom
Even though my heart will break
I can't presume.
Even though this process is painful to see
I know the choice is hers finally.
It will be fine,
She's not truly mine
So I'm letting her grow.

                    Knowing deep in my heart
                    That it's all a part
                    Of letting her go.

                              SCENE 19

The past

Tracy enters Mum's place. It is empty

Tracy (*calling*) Mum. Muuuu-um!

She sees the gift and an envelope on the table. It is a Tracy-sized black fairy outfit

   Goblinda!

She grabs the envelope and opens it. She reads the card aloud

   "From one free spirit to another. Goodbye darling. Yours forever, Mum." (*Beat*) No!

She calls loudly for Mum again

   Mum! Muuuum!

Horrible silence

   She left me again. (*She sings*)

No. 17: Hollywood Mum Reprise

                    There's a place where dreams are made
                    Where the bright lights never fade
                    And the stars are on parade
                    Each night.
                    It's the place that I go to
                    When I'm feeling sad and blue
                    It's the one thing I can do
                    All right.
                    You are beautiful
                    My superstar

Lighting up my darkest night from where you are
I'll snap you
And trap you
And stay with you until
I make you
And shape you
My dreams are with me still.
I hoped we could be happy here
How could I have been so dumb!
Now you'll always have to stay
My Hollywood mum.

SCENE 20

The past

Tracy enters Cam's space. Cam is there

Cam Is something wrong?
Tracy No!
Cam I thought you were staying with your mum this weekend.
Tracy If you want me to go just say so!
Cam What happened?
Tracy Nothing happened!
Cam Hey, it's me. You can tell me.
Tracy I just decided to stay here for a while, OK?!
Cam Something must have happened to upset you so much …
Tracy I'm not upset! It's hay fever.
Cam Tracy …
Tracy Don't start nagging about how right you were about my mum, 'cos you're wrong! She got a job and had to leave in a hurry.
Cam What kind of job?
Tracy The usual kind.
Cam Where?
Tracy You have no right to interrogate me!
Cam I've put a lot into your care, surely I can ——
Tracy All right! If you must know …
Cam Go on.
Tracy She … (*She can't say the truth*) She's going to Hollywood again.
Cam No. Not that, Tracy.
Tracy Are you calling me a liar?

Cam I just want our times together to be real.
Tracy I've got homework. (*She starts to leave*)
Cam Wait!

Tracy stops

Tracy, if you want to stay with me you have to be honest with me.
Tracy I don't have to anything!
Cam You're right. It's your choice.
Tracy Or?
Cam I've got rights too and I don't like being lied to.
Tracy You're against my mum, you always have been!
Cam I'm against us being unhappy because of some made up ——
Tracy Fine, I won't make you unhappy any more! I should have known
you'd dump me again! I hate you! I never want to see you again! (*She
screams the Beaker scream*)

SCENE 21

The present

*Tracy continues to scream. Tracy, Peter, Justine, Elaine and Kids are
on stage*

All Tracy Beaker's back!
Tracy (*to audience*) Back where we started. Binned, dumped and
rubbished. Definitely The End. Please take care not to leave your
personal belongings behind — and that means him over there with the
annoying sweet wrappers!
Peter You can't end the story there either.
Tracy Not again! Someone get the fly killer!
Peter They'll be wanting a happy ending. You said so yourself.
Tracy It will be happy one day. When my mum sends for me to come
to Hollywood.
Peter What if she doesn't ... (*He loses his nerve*) ... If, for some
unexpected reason, she couldn't send for you.
Tracy That's not going to happen.
Peter But if it did. Like if she got some terrible disease from filming in
the jungle or she got captured by aliens.
Tracy Then I'd stay here until I'm sixteen, Frogspawn, because it's the
law — then get a very good job ——
Peter How are you going to get a good job if you don't stay at school?

Tracy (*raising her voice*) — and a fantastic flat and a big pink car and everything I want! And you definitely won't be there giving my ears grief every five minutes!

Peter Don't shout at me. I don't like it.

Tracy Well don't ask stupid questions!

Peter Tracy, I've always stuck by you, haven't I?

Tracy Yeah, like pondweed to a drowning cat.

Peter breaks

Peter (*yelling*) That's it, Tracy Beaker — no more!

Everyone is now watching

Tracy Huh?

Peter I'm not a weed or a mouse or a bee or a bug, Tracy! I'm tired of it.

Tracy I don't mean anything by it.

Peter I used to believe that. I used to see a kind Tracy underneath all that anger. The kid that was hurting as much as I was. But I can't find that Tracy any more!

Tracy So? Join the queue and dump me.

Peter Only one person ever dumped you. And you know who.

Elaine Peter, let's leave Tracy to — erp!

Justine, outrageously, clamps Elaine's mouth shut

Tracy (*to Peter*) That's not true.

Peter And ever since your mum dumped you when you were just a little baby ——

Tracy My mum didn't dump me! She was ——

Peter Get real, Tracy. She was never in Hollywood. She dumped you big time. And you've made sure you dumped everyone else ever since. Including all your foster parents, including Cam — including me!

Tracy When did I ever dump you?

Peter Almost every time you speak to me. (*Beat*) All I ever did to you was give you my friendship. And I get nothing back!

Tracy I am your f ——

Peter No. Tracy Beaker can't be my friend. She can't be anyone's friend. She doesn't know how.

Peter leaves

Everyone looks at Tracy, waiting for the scream. She puffs up and opens her mouth — and a tiny squeak comes out. She tries again — nothing. Tracy's face crumples and she starts to cry — then blubber. All watch in amazement. Justine walks up to her

Justine Hay fever?

Tracy shakes her head

Tracy Beaker's crying?

Tracy nods. It looks like Justine is going to sneer and taunt. But instead she puts her arms round Tracy. Tracy simply leans on her, helpless and blubbering. Elaine is torn. She hurries to hug both girls then stops

Elaine What about professional boundaries?!

Elaine dithers. All the kids run and make a group hug with the girls. Elaine breaks and hugs too. Then suddenly all the kids duck and scatter and she's left standing with arms out and nobody in them.

Elaine hurries off

Tracy wipes her eyes

Tracy (*to the audience*) I should be in the medical books. That was the worst case of hay fever ever known! (*To an audience member*) If I say it was hay fever it was hay fever! (*To all*) There's a couple of things I need to do.

SCENE 22

The present

Tracy finds Peter

Peter I won't blame you if you don't want to speak to me again. I'm a disgrace.
Tracy One day I'm gonna have to shake old people out of your system.
Peter What do you mean?
Tracy "Get real"?! "I'm a disgrace"? Pass the parcel?

Peter I can't help it.

Tracy I bet Nan or Auntie Vi also said "don't go to bed on an argument."

Peter Auntie Vi.

Tracy She's right.

Peter She is?

Tracy Well?

Peter I apologize. I didn't mean to hurt you.

Tracy Honestly!

Peter What?

Tracy You've got to ask for more, Oliver!

Peter I don't understand it when you say that.

Tracy Yes you do. Ask for more.

Peter I —

Tracy Ask for more!!

She shouts it again and again

Peter Be quiet! (*He gathers his courage*) Tracy Beaker. Will you be my proper true friend? And never call me names again?

Tracy I'd be honoured, Mr Ingham.

SCENE 23

The present. Cam's place

Cam, Peter and Kids are on stage

Tracy enters

Tracy Hi.

Cam is near tears

I've got something important to tell you.

Cam You have?

Tracy My mum's not in Hollywood. She never was. She's here.

Cam Here?

Tracy walks up to Cam and touches her

Tracy Right here.

They hold each other

The box of chocolates on legs appears and cockily takes a bow

Peter (*to the audience*) Now it's finished.
Elaine (*off; yelling*) Oh no it's not!!

  Elaine enters. She is very put out

I'm the social worker here and I haven't sung yet!

No. 18: Elaine the Pain

Elaine sings operatically

> If your problems start to get you down
> If you feel you're going quite insane
> Just call on me and I will come around
> You'll have a lovely little session with
>   ... aaah (*Cadenza*) ... Elaine.

Kids   Elaine the Pain!
               She gets inside your brain.
               Until you feel that you could
               Throw a fit.
               Elaine the Pain
               She really earns her name
               She makes you feel like blowing it.

Elaine   I'm fully qualified you must agree
               I've a framed first-class psychology degree
               And even if you've got ADHD
               You'll pay attention in your session with Elaine.

               'Cos I'm caring
               I'm sharing
               Your pain I'll be bearing
               When you open your heart to me
               I've patience
               In shed loads
               Self-help books I've read loads,
               Just watch me work and you will see
               I never blow my top, I'm always calm and in control.

	Before I lose my cool I count to ten.
	Two three four five six seven ...
Kids	Nine eight seven six five four ...

Elaine
A shoulder to cry on
A soft couch to lie on
When you come and see Elaine.

Kids
Elaine the Pain
It's pointless to complain
She makes a three act show of it.

Elaine
It's not your fault that you are in a home
You prob'ly have acute displacement syndrome
And because I have a caring chromosome
I'll work on you 'til you are an Elaine clone.

Kids
Eurrgh!

Elaine
'Cos I'm caring
I'm sharing
Your pain I'll be bearing
When you open your heart to me
I've patience
In shed loads
Self-help books I've read loads.
Just watch me work and you will see
I never blow my top, I'm always calm and in control.
Before I lose my head I count to ten
Two three four five six seven.

Kids
Elaine the Pain,
She gets inside your brain
She makes you feel that you could throw a fit.
Elaine the Pain
She really earns her name
She makes you feel like blowing it.
She never blows her top
She always counts to ten,
Nine eight seven six five four.

Elaine
A shoulder to cry on
A soft couch to lie on.

Kids
Elaine the Pain
She's driving us insane.

Elaine	When you come and see her
Kids	Wouldn't want to be her
Elaine	So come and see her
Kids	Wish she'd disappear
All	Elaine
Kids	The Pain!

Elaine (*speaking; to the audience*) Now it's finished.

All exit

Finale: characters enter, sing a part of their song and take their bow:

Peter enters

No. 19: Finale

Peter   You don't have to be perfect
Or even the best you can be.
You don't have to go set the world on fire
Just listen to me.
If Tracy's not the one then it is easy to see.
There's lots of other fishes in the deep blue sea.

Justine enters

Justine   It's all right,
I don't mind,
There's nothing else I want to do.
So I might
Spend my time
Counting off the minutes
While I'm waiting for you.

Elaine enters

Elaine   Aaah ... (*Cadenza*)

Mum enters

Mum   Adore me
Implore me
And I'll shine brighter still. So snap me,

Unwrap me,
Your dreams I will fulfil.
I could have been a great novelist
But how could I waste this bum?
And I know just how to be a
Hollywood Mum.

Cam enters

Cam   There's something about her
                       Something that is wild and free.
                       There's something about her
                       Makes me think that maybe she could be ...

Tracy enters

All   There's something about her
                       Something leads my heart astray
                       There's something about her
                       She's the one who'll take my pain away.
                       Someone tell me please
                       How can I make her stay
                       How can I make her stay?

CURTAIN

FURNITURE AND PROPERTY LIST

Further dressing may be added at the director's discretion

ACT I
SCENE 1

On stage: No furniture or property required

Off stage: Wheelie bin (**Elaine** and **Tracy**)
Belongings including a notebook with her life story in it
(**Tracy**)

SCENE 2

On stage: As before

SCENE 3

On stage: As before

SCENE 4

On stage: As before

SCENE 5

Set: Bean bag

SCENE 6

Strike: Bean bag

Off stage: Jar of worms (**Kid**)
Bucket (**Elaine**)

SCENE 7

On stage: No furniture or property required

Off stage: Wet sheet (**Peter**)
Food (**Tracy**)

SCENE 8

On stage: As before

SCENE 9

On stage: As before

Personal: **Elaine**: clipboard and pen

SCENE 10

On stage: As before

SCENE 11

On stage: As before

Off stage: Magazine (**Kid**)

SCENE 12

On stage: As before

SCENE 13

On stage: As before

Off stage: Plastic bag containing Mickey Mouse clock (**Dad**)
                Large Mickey Mouse clock on legs (**SM**)

SCENE 14

On stage: As before

SCENE 15

On stage: As before

Personal: **Tracy**: whistle

SCENE 16

On stage: As before

SCENE 17

On stage: As before

SCENE 18

Set: Notebooks and pencils

Off stage: Gilt chair (**Lady Writer/SM**)
Large notebook, pen (**Lady Writer**)

SCENE 19

Strike: Notebooks and pencils

Set: Bean bag
Foam rubber therapy bat

Personal: **Cam**: notebook

ACT II

SCENE 1

Strike: Foam rubber therapy bat

SCENE 2

Strike: Bean bag

Personal: **Cam**: letter

SCENE 3

On stage: No furniture or property required

SCENE 4

Set: Bean bag

SCENE 5

Strike: Bean bag

SCENE 6

Set:	Table Two chairs Burgers
Personal:	**Cam**: handbag containing Mickey Mouse pen

SCENE 7

Strike:	Table Two chairs Burgers
Off stage:	Mickey Mouse pen (**Tracy**)

SCENE 8

On stage:	No furniture or property required

SCENE 9

Set:	Telephone
Off stage:	Large, pink-ribboned, heart-shaped box of chocolates on legs (**SM**)

SCENE 10

On stage:	As before
Personal:	**Tracy**: locket or charm

SCENE 11

Strike:	Telephone

SCENE 12

On stage:	No furniture or property required

SCENE 13

Set:	Present containing small fairy outfit

SCENE 14

Strike: Present containing small fairy outfit

SCENE 15

On stage: No furniture or property required

SCENE 16

On stage: As before

Personal: **Mum:** lipstick

SCENE 17

On stage: As before

SCENE 18

On stage: As before

Off stage: Present containing Tracy-sized fairy outfit, envelope (**Mum**)

SCENE 19

On stage: Present containing Tracy-sized fairy outfit, envelope

SCENE 20

Strike: Present containing Tracy-sized fairy outfit, envelope

SCENE 21

On stage: No furniture or property required

SCENE 22

On stage: As before

SCENE 23

On stage: As before

Off stage: Large box of chocolates on legs (**SM**)

LIGHTING PLOT

Practical fittings required: nil

ACT I

To open: General interior lighting

Cue 1	**Tracy**: Chapter "Man The Lifeboats!" *Fade lights*	(Page 15)
Cue 2	**Peter**: "That's just her syndrome talking." *Bring up lights*	(Page 17)

ACT II

To open: General interior lighting

No cues

EFFECTS PLOT

ACT I

ACT II